Could it be...?
It's deep enough...
I can't see the bottom from the shallow end.
Aha! A side passage!
I've got it!
This must be the way out.
But it's a long way, underwater.
I don't think I can hold my breath long enough.
But I have no choice. I have to try.
Hhhh-hrrp
Hhhr-hhr

So far...

My lungs are bursting!

My air's getting stale....

Urgh! Come on, Chinmi!

I'm past my limit!!

Just a little more...

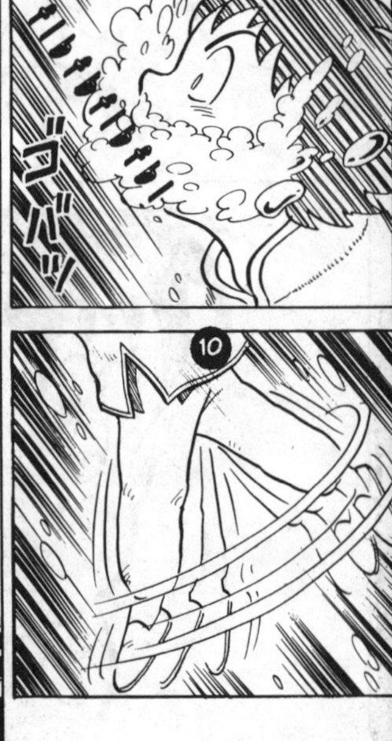

SWOOSH

Phew
Phew
Urrrcgh
Whew

Ugh...

coughcoughcoughcough

Argh! That was awful!
Hhhr- Hhhr- hhr
hhr
I really thought I was a dead man...

That must have been it - the final test...

WAAAAAGH!

...

Wh...What!?
A statue of a warrior. Must be here to surprise me...

That light...
Whey-hey!
The Exit!

Phew
I've done it...

The warrior statue is guarding the exit.

k you for your noble efforts.
You have made the
rest of my journey easy.

Heh heh

So, the lessons of Mount Shen are finally finished.

shik

WHAT WAS THAT?
PLING

WAAAAGH!!!

SWOOSH

SWISH
Yagh!

Ouch!
That hurt...
What's a statue doing attacking me!?

I'm sure I'd remember if I'd made you angry!!

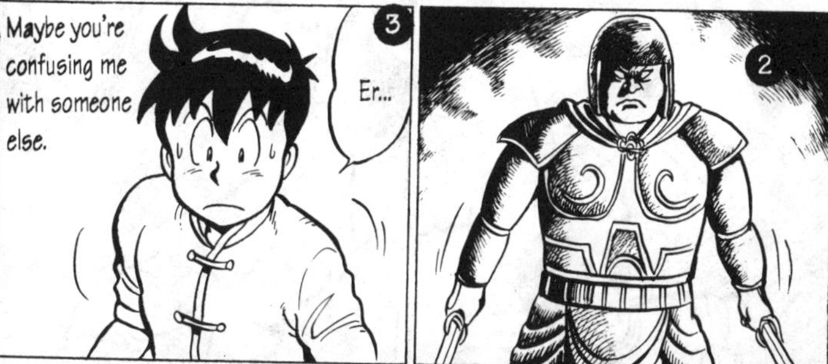
Er...
Maybe you're confusing me with someone else.

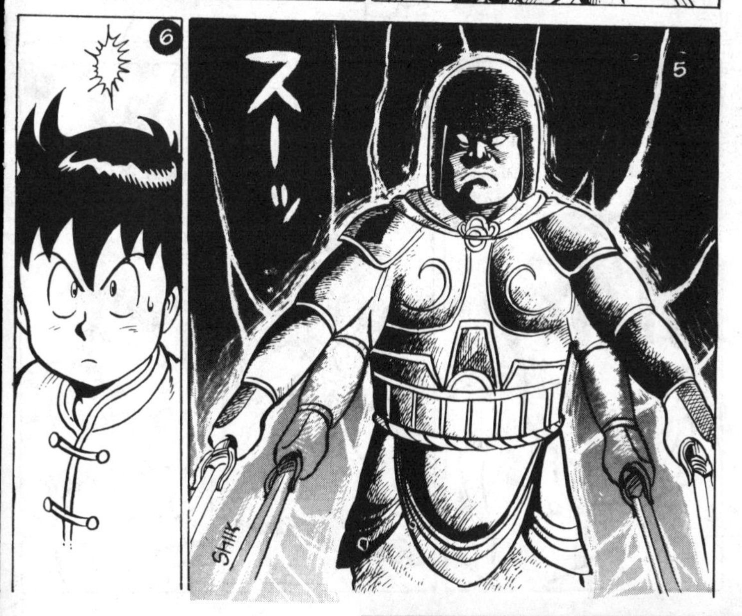
スーッ
SHIIK

Uh!? Its hands!
A thousand hands, just like Guan Yin, the Goddess of Mercy.

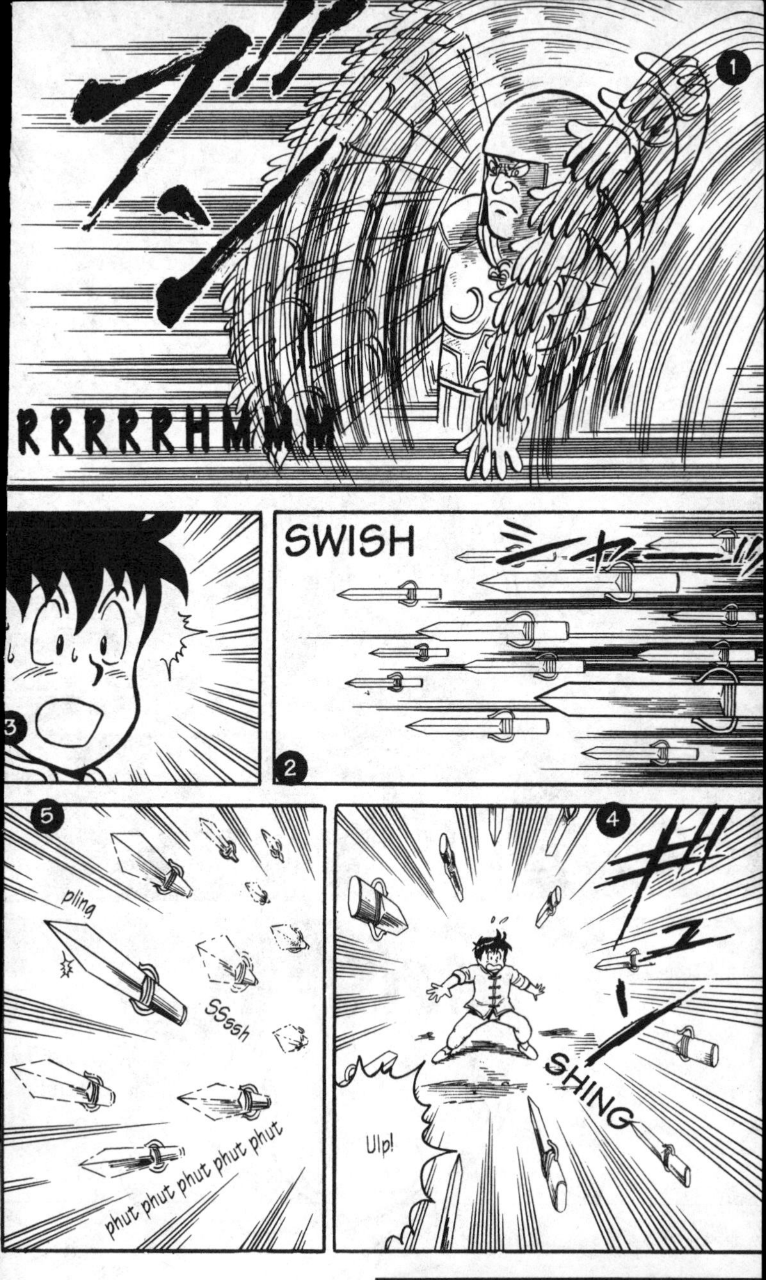
RRRRRHMMM
SWISH
pling
SSssh
phut phut phut phut phut
Ulp!
SHING

Eh!?
ploingggg...
THWAP
All the other knives disappeared....
Only one was real. The others must have been illusions...
He's a scary-looking guy...
But if only one of the knives is real...
all I have to do is work out which...
...and then avoid it!
So! Victory comes to the swift!
swoosh

oops!
swish
Damn! He's bound to get me at close quarters...!
I'll need something to make him keep his distance...
This should do it...
CATCH!!
swoosh
KLONG
crunch
patter
patter
don't believe it! What kind f thing s this!?

Uh-oh...
No way
out!
He's trying
it again!!
SWOOSH

pling
crump
thwip
kachi
I can't get out of his range...
...but what can I do...?

Could it be...?
It's deep enough...
I can't see the bottom from the shallow end.
Aha! A side passage!
I've got it!
This must be the way out.
But it's a long way, underwater.
I don't think I can hold my breath long enough.
But I have no choice. I have to try.
Hhhr-hhr
Hhhh-hrrp

So far...

My lungs are bursting!

My air's getting stale....

Urgh! Come on, Chinmi!

7
I'm past my limit!!

Just a little more...
8

10

11
SWOOSH

Phew
Phew
Urrrcgh
Whew
Ugh...
coughcoughcoughcough

Argh! That was awful!
Hhhr-
Hhhr- hhr
hhr
I really thought I was a dead man...

That must have been it - the final test...

WAAAAAGH!

...

Wh...What!?
A statue of a warrior. Must be here to surprise me...

That light...

The Exit!
Whey-hey!

I've done it...
Phew

The warrior statue is guarding the exit.

k you for your noble efforts. You have made the est of my journey easy.

Heh heh

So, the lessons of Mount Shen are finally finished.

shik

WHAT WAS THAT?
PLING

WAAAAGH!!!

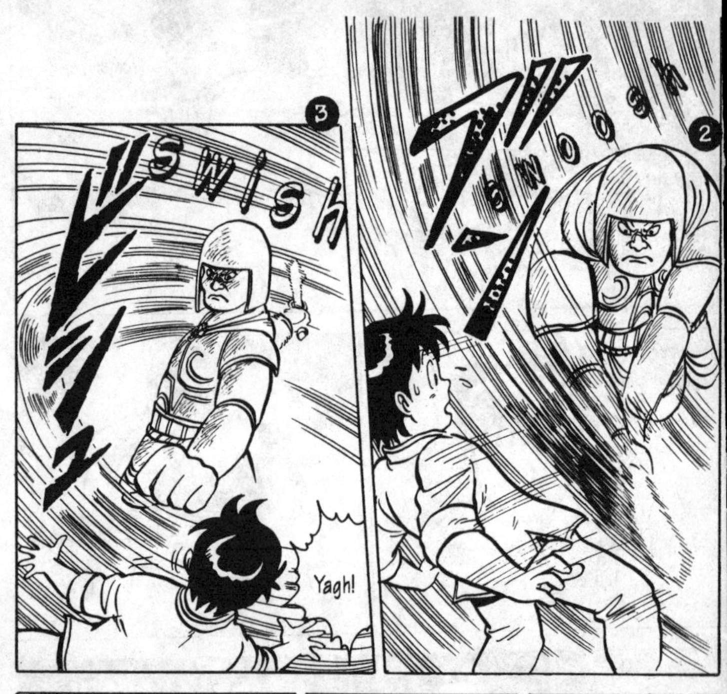
WHOOSH
SWISH
Yagh!

Ouch!
That hurt...
What's a statue doing attacking me!?

1
I'm sure I'd remember if I'd made you angry!!

2

3
Er...
Maybe you're confusing me with someone else.

5
スーッ
SHIIK

6

Uh!? Its hands!
A thousand hands, just like Guan Yin, the Goddess of Mercy.

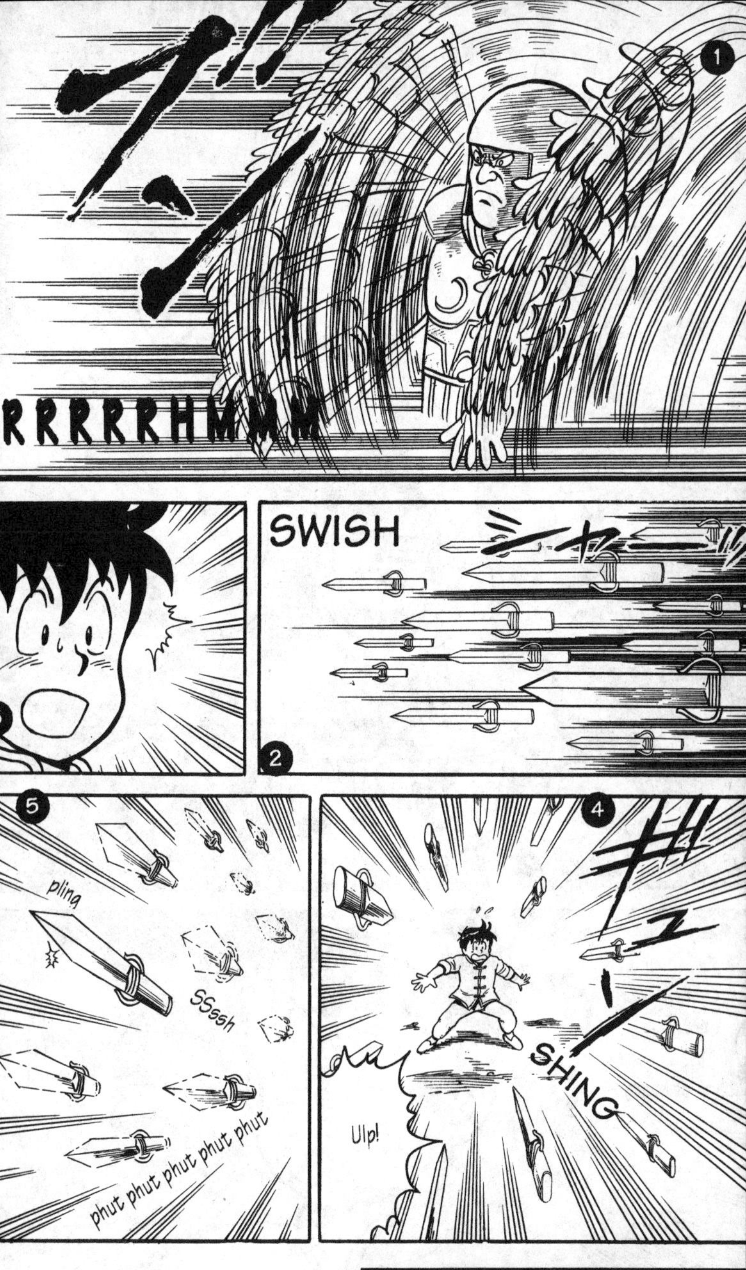
RRRRRRHMMM
SWISH
SHING
Ulp!
pling
SSsssh
phut phut phut phut phut

Eh!?
THWAP
ploinggg...

All the other knives disappeared....
Only one was real. The others must have been illusions...

He's scary lookin guy..

But if only one of the knives is real...

all I hav to do i work ou which.
...and then avoid it!

So! Victory comes to the swift!
swoosh

oops!
swish
Damn! He's bound to get me at close quarters...!
I'll need something to make him keep his distance...
This should do it...
CATCH!!
swoosh
KLONG
crunch
patter
patter
don't believe it!
hat kind
thing
this!?

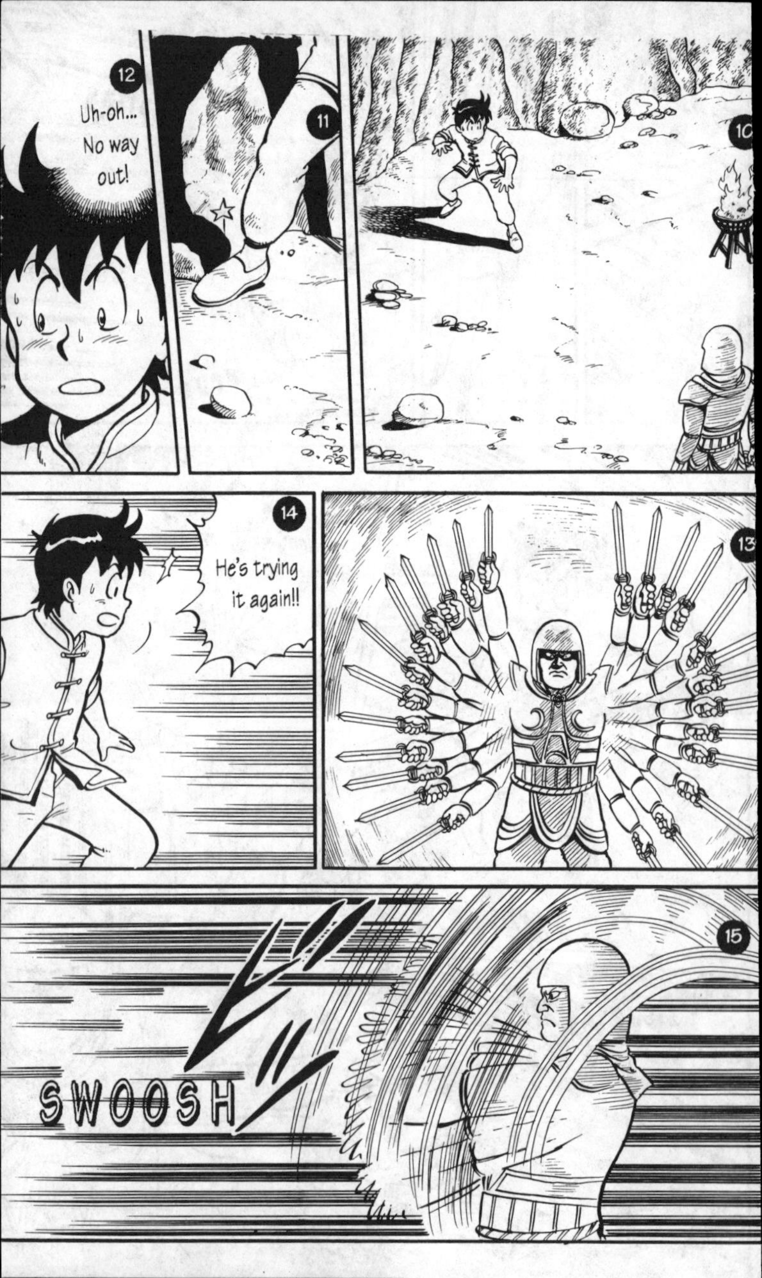
Uh-oh...
No way
out!
He's trying
it again!!
SWOOSH

pling
crump
thwip
kachik
I can't get out of his range...
...but what can I do...?

hhr
Hhhr-hhr
Hhhr-hhr
hhr
Hhhr-

Hhhr-hhr
kerchink kerchink

He's trying to close the distance! There's no way I can get out of his way at close range...!
Hhhr-hhr
If that happens I'm dead!

ズシャ
There has to be a way of telling the real knives from the fake ones...
kerchink

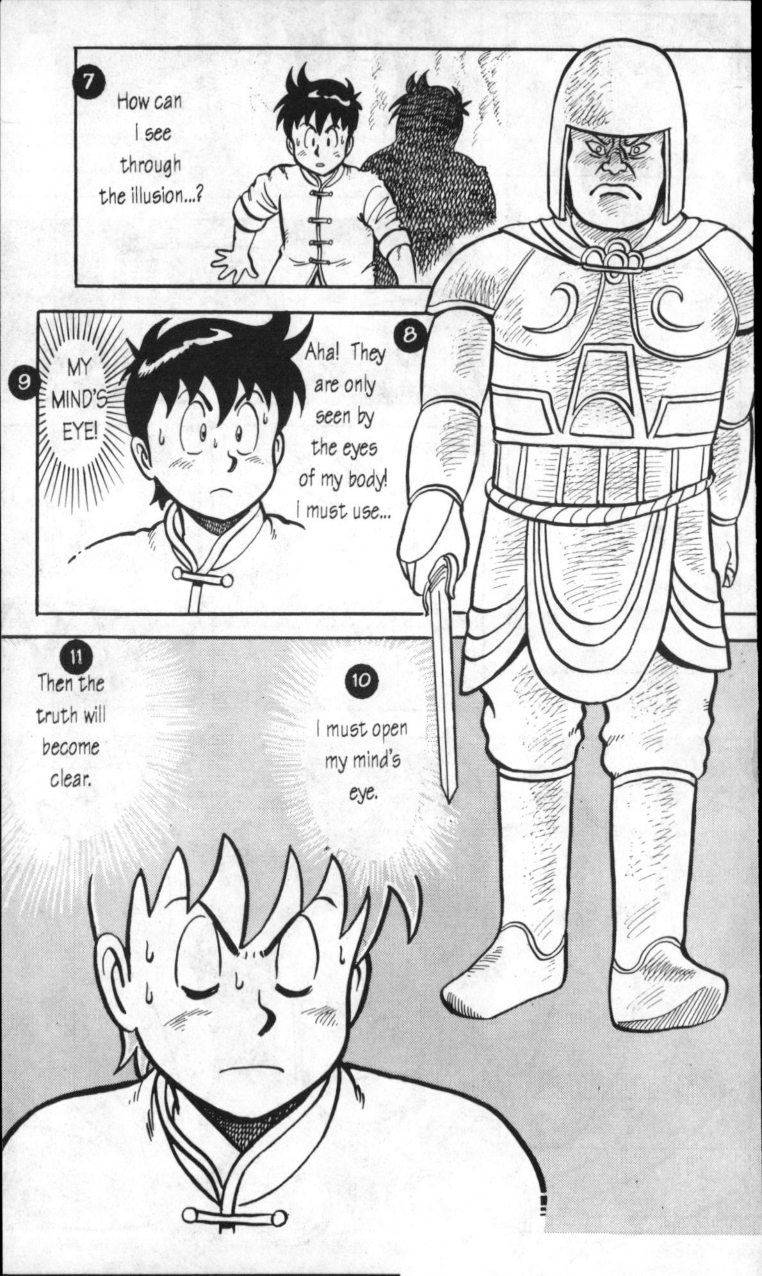
7
How can I see through the illusion...?
8
Aha! They are only seen by the eyes of my body! I must use...
9
MY MIND'S EYE!
10
I must open my mind's eye.
11
Then the truth will become clear.

PHEW

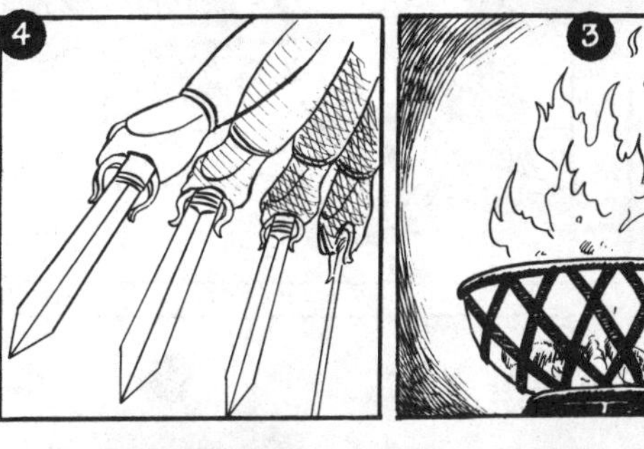

Pling

clink

SWOOOSH

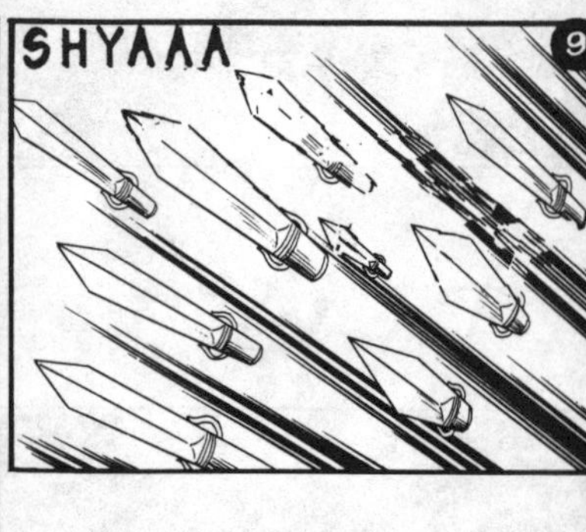
SHYAAA

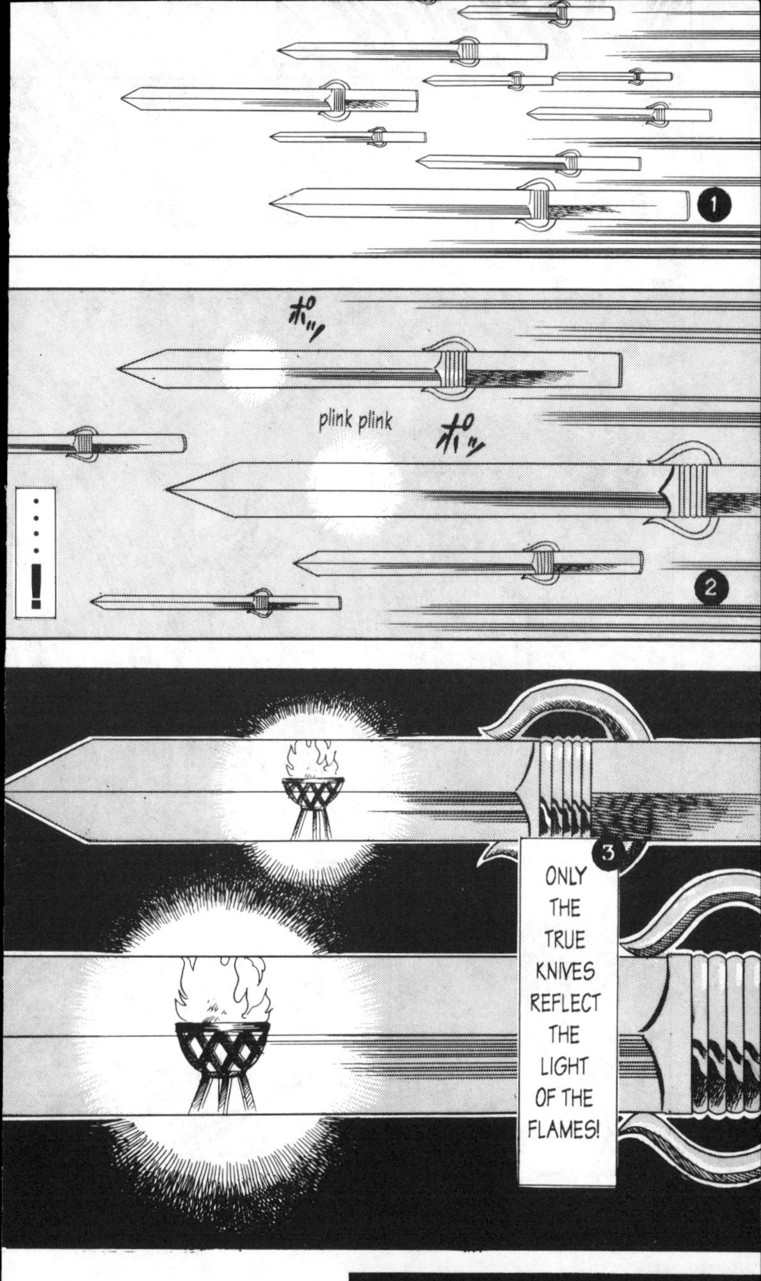
ポッ
plink plink
ポッ
....!
ONLY THE TRUE KNIVES REFLECT THE LIGHT OF THE FLAMES!

PLING
SWISH

!?
GOT IT!!
This time there are **two** knives!

SWISH...
THWAP

Now it's my turn...
clink
clink
SWOOSH
tlilihhh...

TOO EASY, PEBBLE PANTS!
WAP!!
thwip
boing

shik

swish
crunch

SHONK

SMACK

Say your prayers!

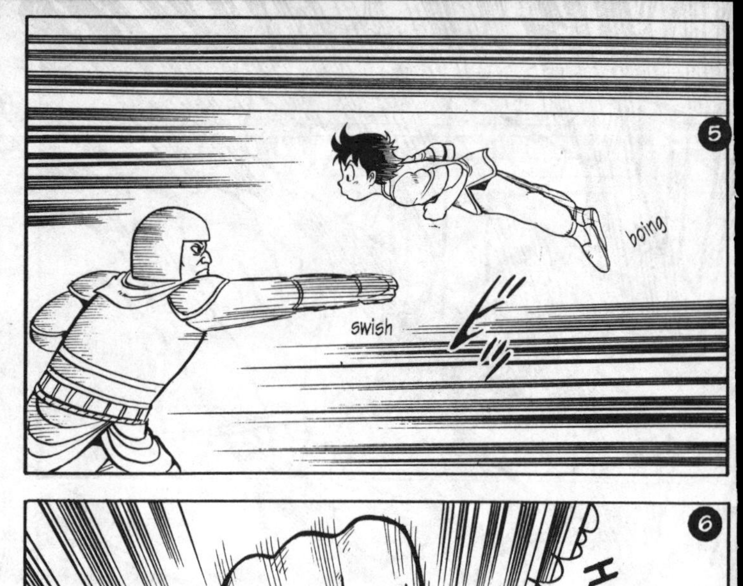
boing
swish

HAAAAAGH!!!

KLONG!

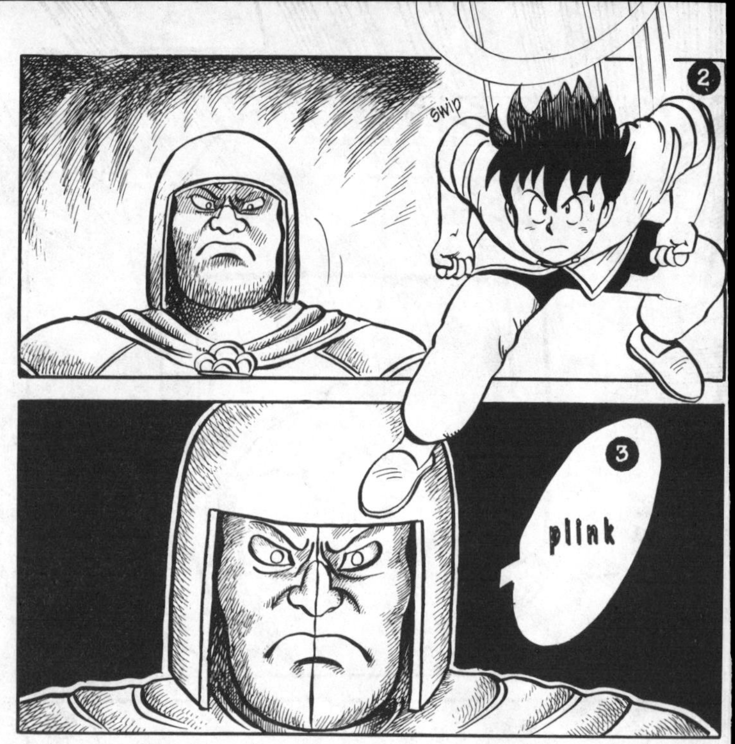
swip
plink

Its face....
PACHINK

Er... uh... um...?

You have learned well, young Chinmi...

Old Master!!
I really had to work hard.

That was a pretty dangerous test. I dread to think what the final one will be...

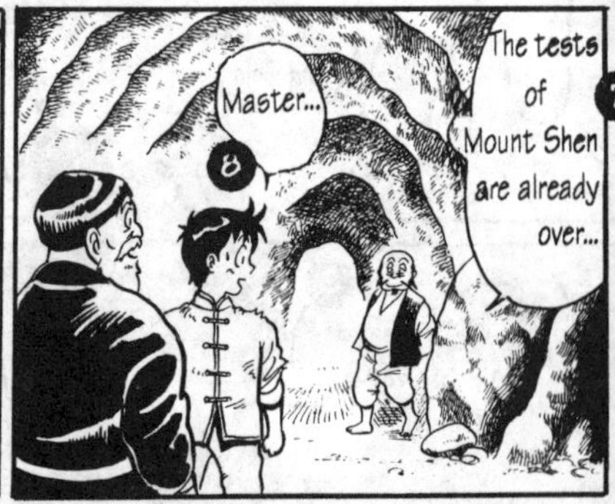
The tests of Mount Shen are already over...
Master...

You may not think so, but...
...you have just proved yourself, Chinmi.

The Zen Master knew all along...

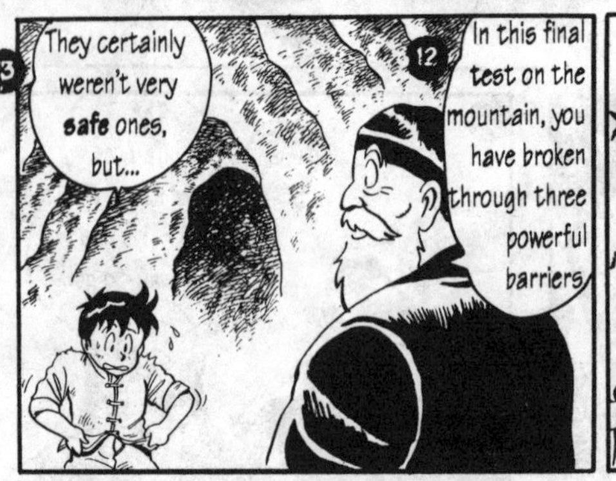
In this final test on the mountain, you have broken through three powerful barriers
They certainly weren't very safe ones, but...

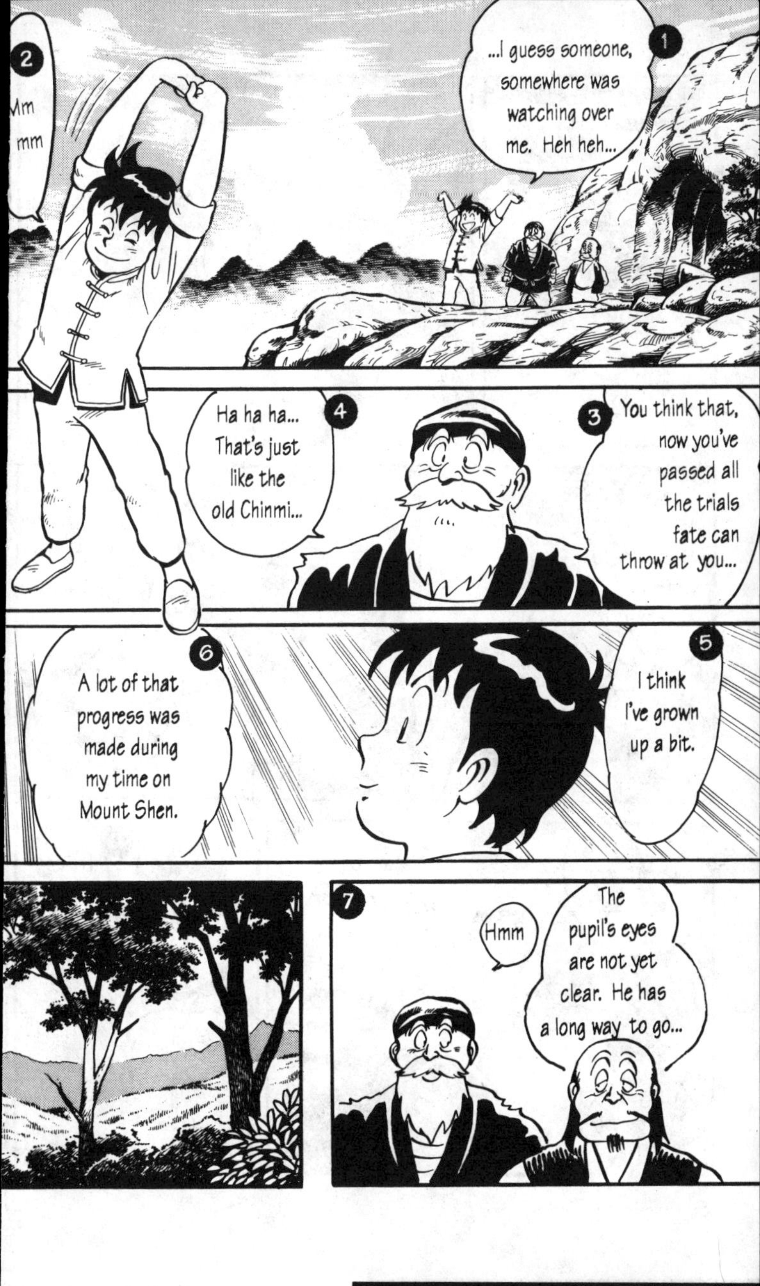
...I guess someone, somewhere was watching over me. Heh heh...
Mm mm
You think that, now you've passed all the trials fate can throw at you...
Ha ha ha... That's just like the old Chinmi...
I think I've grown up a bit.
A lot of that progress was made during my time on Mount Shen.
Hmm
The pupil's eyes are not yet clear. He has a long way to go...

Master Tiandao, I can never repay you for all you have taught me.

Chinmi, my student, your most important lessons are yet to come.
From now on, you must continually refine your mind and body.

Yes, Master.
I will remember your words as long as I live.

...

Well, Master Tiandao...
Thank you again...

Keep going, Chinmi... You have quite a way to go...

Eeek!
Gokuwa!

Gokuwa's here too!?
I thought you weren't coming back!

Wave with me, Gokuwa!

Master Tiandao...!
Eeek eeek!!

Master Tiandao...!

Master Tiandao

Thank you...!

10
I'm very glad
to have met
you, Chinmi...
The End of Chapter One

Chapter Two
Enter the Iron Man Ryukai

This is a lively place - so many people!
You wouldn't have noticed that before you went to Mount Shen.
Luverly chickens!
That's daylight robbery.
The eating-places are that way...
Let's go
Let's go

まんじゅう
I'll have two meat buns.
What'll it be?

The same for me.
EEK!
Shut it, Gokuwa! You can have a little piece of mine.
EEK
A whole day of walking and I'm exhausted!
Heh heh...
I feel great.
Due to your training on Mount Shen, eh...

I did quite a lot...
I can hardly believe I did all that.
Well, each day from now on you'll have to...
...try and recreate those lessons.
Hey! Get out of my way!
Watch where you're going, idiot!
Oi! Get me some more wine!
I'm still thirsty!
Hahahahaa
Wine! Give me some wine!
What are you looking at!?
Hey! Barman!! Give us some booze, and quick about it!!
Looks like they've had a few too many...
Yes...they are bound together by the madness of drink.

1
Don't do anything to make them angry.
2
Oof
3
4
clink
5
Heh heh. That was close.
6
Hey, little monk! That wass-a pretty nifty ssave!
7
Gulp
Er...It was nothing really.
8
9
Bet you think you're good at fighting, too...!?

Nothing makes me madder than a brat who thinks he knows Kung Fu.
You should leave the fighting to real men!
HEY! Did you hear me!?
If you're a real man, perhaps you should act like one...
You impudent little squirt! You'd better watch your mouth!
Leave the boy alone! What's the point?
Shut up, grandad!!
SMACK
What's that!?
Get off!!
You're sitting in our seats!

Got anything to say, mister!?
Hehehehe
N-No... Put me down...
You're disturbing the customers. Please leave them alone.
That's not disturbing the customers.
THIS IS!! HAHA!
SMASH!
KRASH
RRARGH!
No fighting!
Don't mess up my shop!

This barman is disturbing me! What do you think, boys!?
It's not even a very good bar.
I'm sorry. Please accept this wine.
That's more like it!
Now you're talking!
Hand some of that over...
Unless you want to make me angry...

Chinmi...
Leave this to me...

Hey, pipsqueak! You're asking for trouble!
SWATCH

Look! There's a cow in the sky.

What? Where is it?
plok

Eh!?

Hey! Did you spill my wine? You little...
No! Wait, I'll get it back for you!

SWOOSH
Wait for it...

I said I'd give it back...

...didn't I?
CRUMP

I don't think he'll be needing this.
My head...

Heh heh...
That's amazing...
Wow
clap-clap-clap

I'm going to rip you to bits, little monk...!!
You want to try again?

HYAAAGH!
swip swip
foosh
swish
RGLE!!
SPLAT!!
And now it's...
My turn!!

Crump!

Phew

Hmm.
clap-clap-clap
Wow!
Wow!
Huh!?

11
Hooray
Hooray
12
13
Yaaay!
Chin-mee!

14

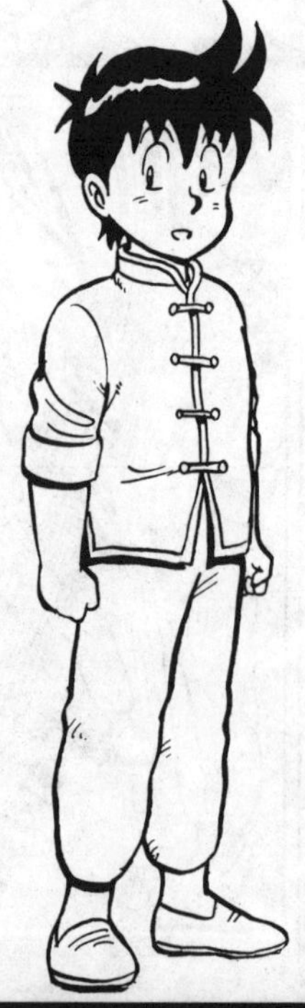

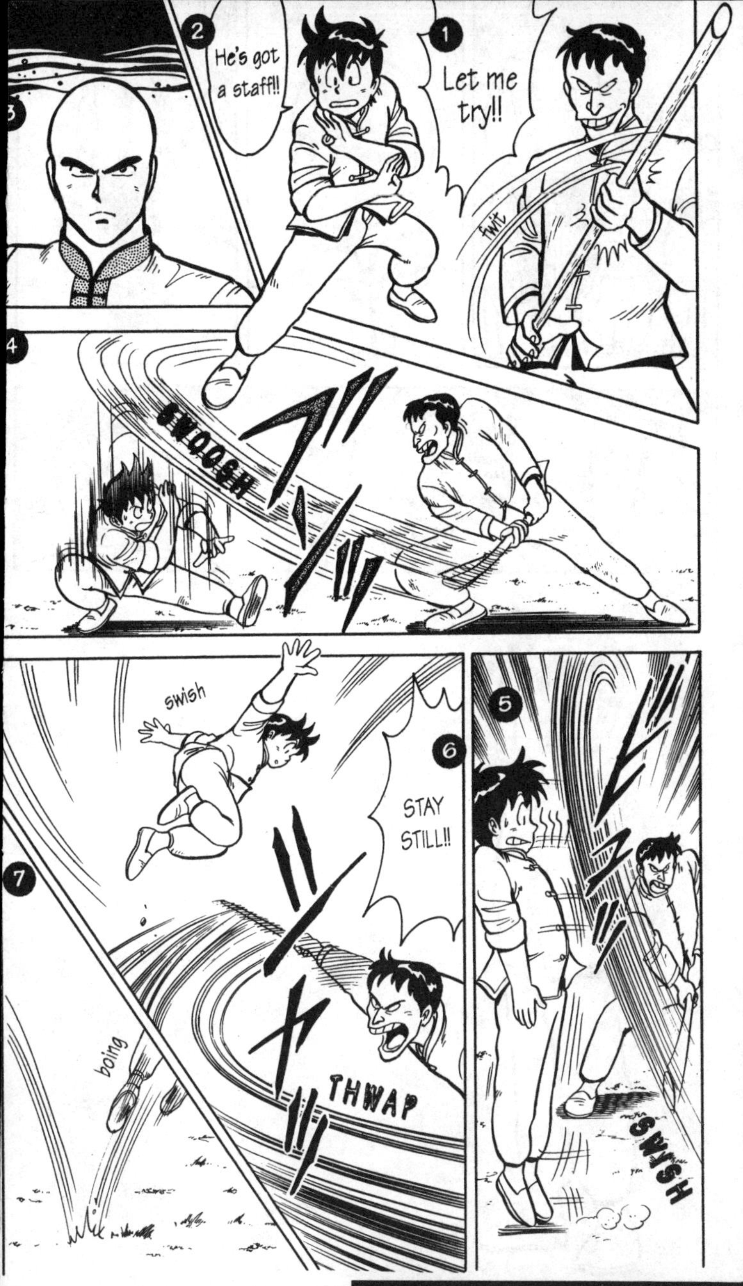
Let me try!!
fwit
He's got a staff!!
SWOOSH
SWISH
swish
STAY STILL!!
THWAP
boing

Two down!
One to go!
clap-clap-clap-clap
YAAAAAAY

Heehee... have the Zen Mast to thank for this..

I'll...

Chinmi's become faster than ever...

.....

chik

Eat this!!

SWISH

I've...got...it...

Ha!

You little twerp!

swip

SPAKK

CRUMP

He did it!!
He's the champ!
CHIN-MEEEEI
Nice one!!
HAHAHA
HAHAHA
Ooooh...my head...

Haha! And I wasn't even trying!!
Chinmi...

Come on, let's get going...
HAHAHAHA!
What a guy!

!?
Could that be the Old Master from the Dailin Temple?

I couldn't have done that before Mount Shen, eh Master?
....
Looks like we're getting closer to Nangao Mountain.
Hn!

Shame we didn't get a chance to finish our food in peace and quiet...
Yeah. I'm getting hungry too
Why don't I try and catch us some fish?
ssh
There they are...
I can see them moving about...
Right...
sploosh
plosh
flup
splish
splosh

Old Master. I've caught loads!

Look at all these!

Well, well, young Chinmi, I hope you're hungry enough to eat them all...

Oh... er... of course.

eep three nd put he rest ack in he stream, ll right..

Chinmi, eh...?

Hhhr-hhr
Hhhr-hhr
Hhhr-hhr
Hhhr-hhr
Here it is! Dailin Temple!
大林寺
I'm back at last!!

CHINMI!!!
CHINMI!!!
JIN
TAN!
Everyone!
You must
be really
pleased to
be back!!
I guess
so...
HAHAH!
When did
you get
to be so
strong!?
Eh!
Hahahaha
Geddoff!
I bet you
forgot all
about us!
Come on!
Tell us about
Mount Shen!

Before tha
I have to
see the Abbot!

Lord Abbot, I have returned!

Chinmi, you're back!
Come in, come closer....

Wha
is it
I want you to meet someone who's just come back from warrior training.

My name is Ryukai. Greetings Chinmi.

Nice to meet you.

And you. But I already know you...

Eh? Where... when...?

On my way here, I saw you in action...

Oh no! Not at the bar?!
Yikes! How embarrassing!

He he heh
It was most impressive.

Thank you...

Each of you have returned to the temple after a long absence...
We'll announce your return, and hold a contest tomorrow. How about that?

12
A contest?
13

14
Yes, I'm sure you'll both want everyone to see what you've learned.
15
The others will want to know what they're letting themselves in for...

16
I expect it'll be a fine match.
17
Yes.

No! Really?
19
You're fighting Ryukai tomorrow!?

He's really powerful. The temple had to send him to another country to train.
He's a scary one.
But surely they'd want the opponents to be more or less equal?
Do you think you can win?
Hey! I went through some pretty tough training on Mount Shen.
ahem.
ponk
Perhaps you could act all stupid to fool him, and then...POW!
We'll have to wait and see...

chirp

rustle

clap-
clap
clap-
clap
clap-
clap
clap
clap-

Right! Let us begin!
The contest is between two who have recently returned to this temple: Ryukai and Chinmi.

Yaaay!
Go for it, Chinmi!
Yaay!
Yaay!
Yaay!
Chin-meeeee!

Don't hold back, Chinmi.

You got it, baldy!

FIGHT!
Yaay!
Yaay!
Yaay!

Hag

Ploing

swip

plonk

shwap

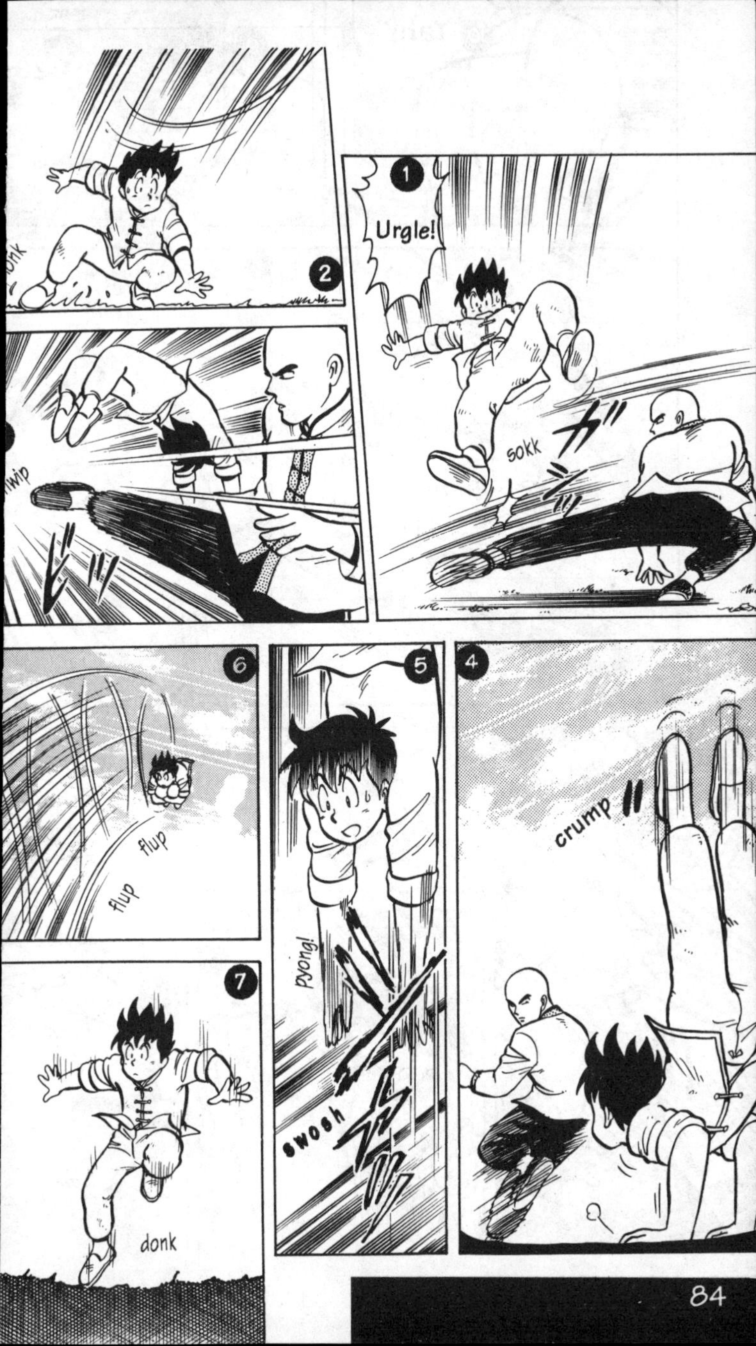
Urgle!
sokk
whip
crump
pyong!
swosh
flup
flup
donk
donk

Yaaay
Yah!
swip
chok
splot
crunch

Chinmi...!
Ouch...
Even now he seems so calm...
Heyaaaagh!
thwip

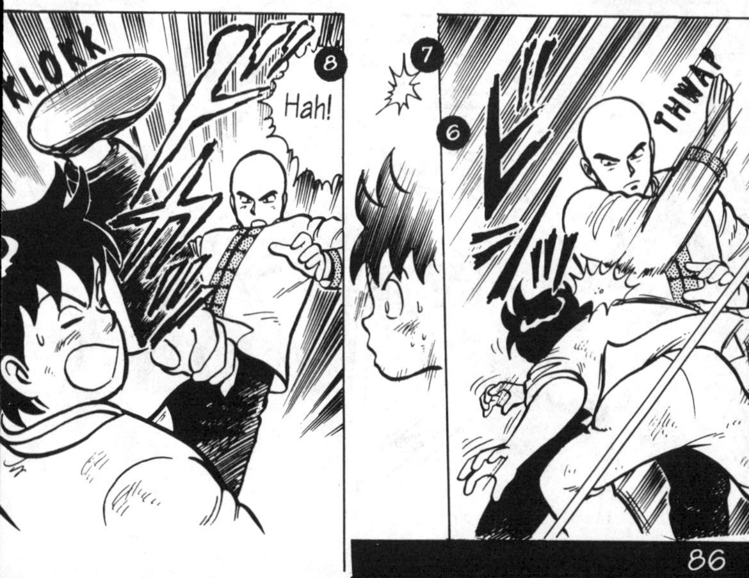

THWAP
Hah!
KLOKK

sputch
Chinmi, what's wrong?
Hhhr-hhr
This is weird...
Hyaagh!
THAP
SMAKK
SMASH

THOKK
I can't do it...
SPLOT
Ksshshshs
Why can't I get him...?
He's too fast for me...even after Mount Shen... And I thought I was doing so well...

...not yet...
Come on, then...
swish
kchik
swoosh
kchak

You may have gone to Mount Shen, but...
SPLUTCH
...THAT'S NOT GOOD ENOUGH!!

crump
GASP
nmi!

Damn... None of my tricks work ...
Hhhr-hhr

Haven't you got it yet, Chinmi?
re's nothing in r head but ceit over r trip to unt Shen.

SWOOSH

Conceit is the enemy of Kung Fu!

BOKK

Hhhr-hhr
I don't know what you're talking about...

Don't you...?
Cast your mind back to yesterday...!?

!?

What about that time at the dumpling shop...
What kind of triumph was it where you DID NOT TRY YOUR BEST!?
Didn't try my best...!?
Chin-meee!
Hooray!

And what was in your head when you brought back all those fish, more than you and the Old Master could possibly eat?
I've caught loads! Look at all these!

8
Kung Fu is not a contest to see how well you can do!

9
If fighters don't know their limits, they'll be defeated.

10
Just don't be overconfident.

11
Overconfidence is like a flaw in your heart...
12
With such a flaw, your fighting suffers. Your moves become predictable, and less forceful.

Now do you understand?
I suppose I have been very proud of myself...
Maybe I've been thinking that I'm unbeatable, just because I've been through the tests of Mount Shen.

7

8
Just how tough are you, Chinmi?!

9

10
LET'S SEE!!
swish

11
And now the real contest begins...

ダダダダ
stomp stomp

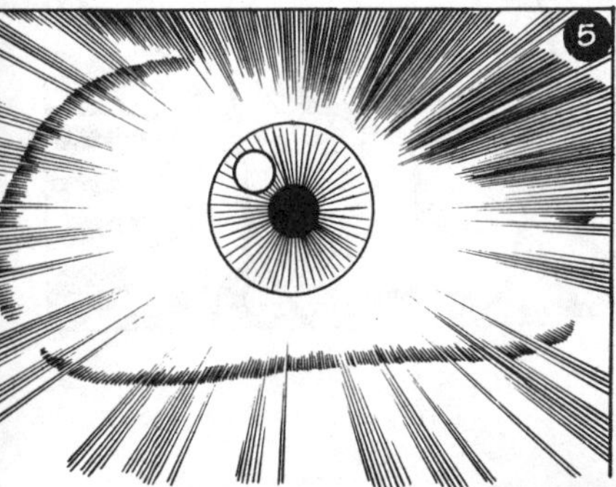

PCHING

WHAM

I... I can't move...

AAAAARGGH!
ulp
plonk

Chinmi...
Chinmi! What's happening!

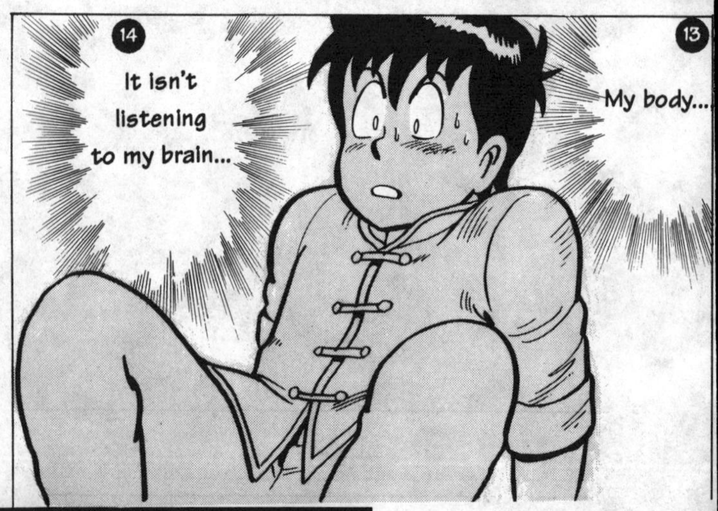
My body...
It isn't listening to my brain...

What... what a trick!!
My body won't move!!
The End of Chapter Two

Chapter Three
Victory for the Spirit

What's wrong with Chinmi?
Why doesn't he just get up...?

......

Huh...

Hhhr-hhr
Hhhr-hhr

I don't know how, but it's like my hands and feet have been tied...
Amazing

There's some kind of energy flowing from Ryukai's entire body.

The Spirit Attack.
Ryukai's body has been imbued with the Way of the Spirit Attack.

This is a secret move, in which he focusses his Qi, or life-force, within his body and then discharges it at his opponent. A truly awesome aspect of the fighting art...

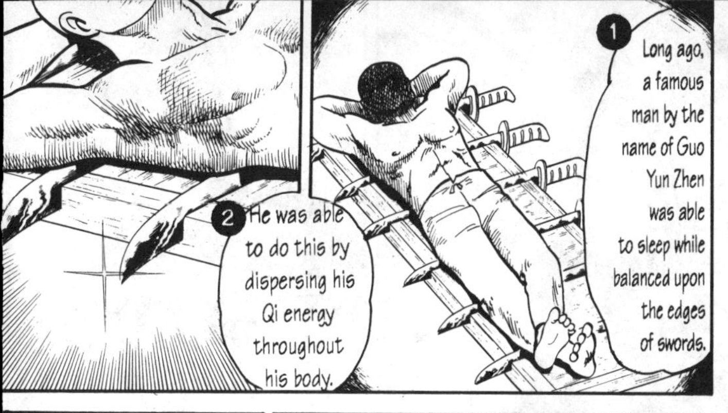
Long ago, a famous man by the name of Guo Yun Zhen was able to sleep while balanced upon the edges of swords.
He was able to do this by dispersing his Qi energy throughout his body.

The true expert was Zheng Shan. He could defeat any opponent by using just one finger. It is said that he could bring down a bird from the sky without touching it.
!

The bird would faint as it encountered his frightful power, and plummet from the sky like a stone.

It is said that we all have the Qi within us. Our Qi may be happy, or forceful, or spirited. With training, you can make your Qi flow like the blood in your veins to create many million, many billions of powers. From ancient times, this has been one of the great secrets of Chinese Kung Fu.
The power that Ryukai is using is just one of the applications of the Spirit Attack.

How will Chinmi cope with the power of the Spirit Attack, I wonder?
Hhhr-hhr

He's standing!

He is still under pressure from the strength of Ryukai's attack...

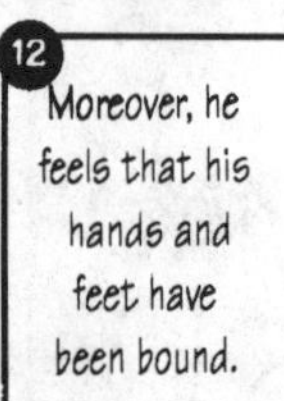
Moreover, he feels that his hands and feet have been bound.

Right...

Against such an attack, he must first prepare his heart... If he does not gather his soul to him and control it, he will be unable to overcome the attack.
He is gaining control of his life-force
Now what's he up to...?

Heehee.. Even if he gathers his strength like that, he still doesn't stand a chance.

Just as I thought. He has studied no other arts but those taught on Mount Shen.

Pheeeew
Hagh!
Shwik
HAGH!
shwip

はあああ
HAAAAGH

Come on, Chinmi! I know you can do it...

Fight back with your own power

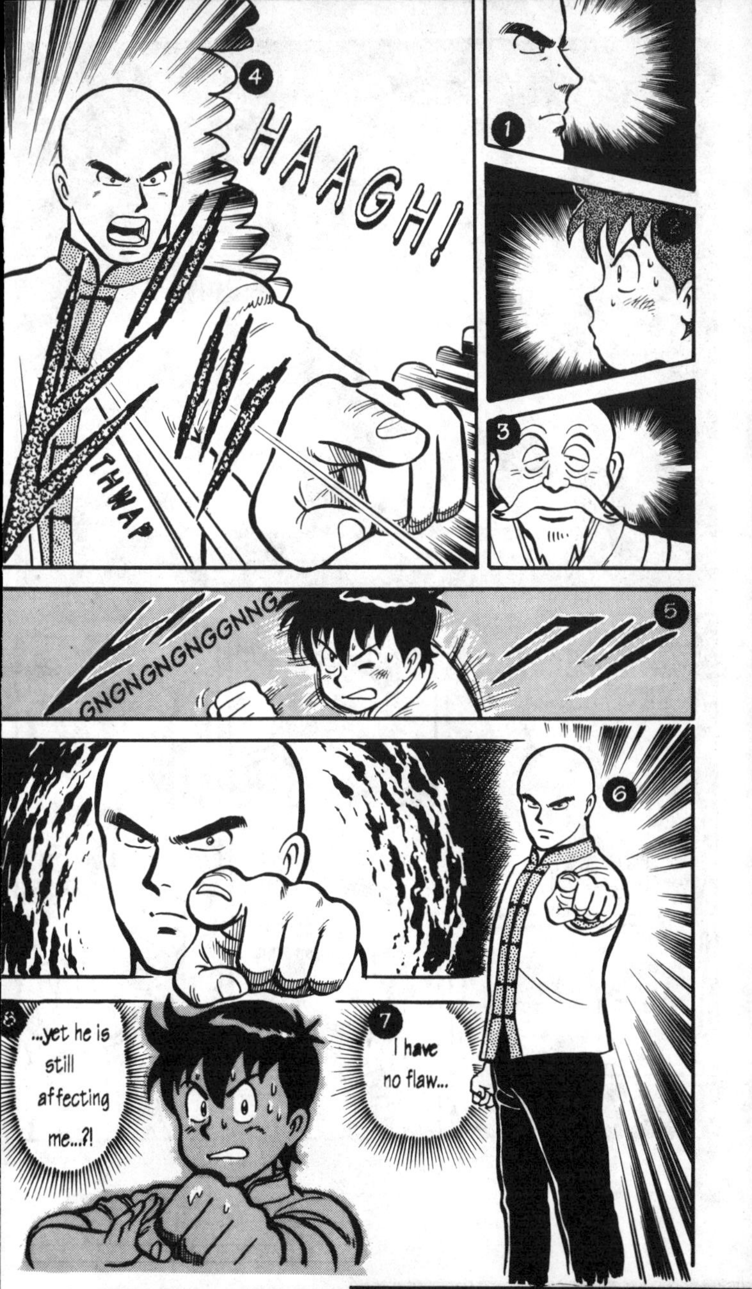
HAAGH!
THWAP
GNGNGNGNGGNNG
I have no flaw...
...yet he is still affecting me...?!

Hhhr
hhr
Hhhr-
hhr

HAAAAGH!!

Urg...
No!

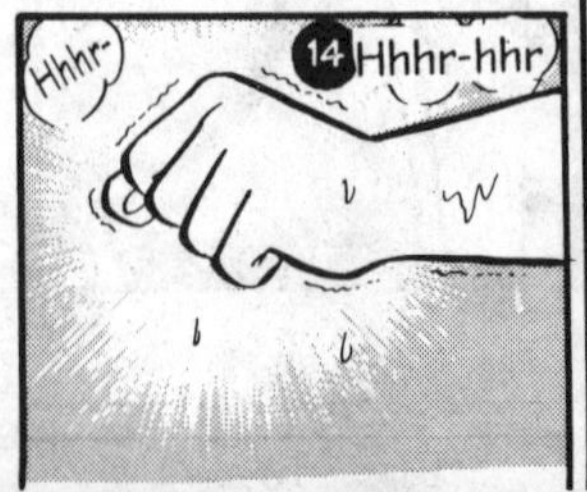
Hhhr-hhr
Hhhr-

Stop there !!

!

スー
swip

URGLE

crump

I forgot to breathe!
I was only watching and I'm sweating like mad...
That was an excellent effort. You put up a good fight, Chinmi..
Nah... You completely wiped me out!

In this combat we have seen the meeting of two schools, straining one against the other.
I think that we have proved once more that speed and skill alone are not enough against the power of the mind.

Ryukai, Chinmi, I thank you both for your display.
clap
clap
clap
clap

Wow... I'm so tired.

Ryukai, what was that move called again?
The Way of Spirit Attack.

Spirit Attack...

I could try and teach you, Chinmi...
..with the strength f will you had ust now, t should e quite asy to earn.

Really!?
Do you really think I'm good enough? Now I know I'm not unbeatable! Heh heh...
Hmph

11 Are you still willing to try?
12 Yes, but...
13 You shouldn't feel ashamed.

14 When your lessons become so tough, only belief in yourself can carry you through.

15 Confidence is still important in some respects...
16 But you have to strike a balance between being over-critical and being over-confident. That's the difficult part.

17 If someone is arrogant
18 ...they must overcome that.

19 I'll study hard! That's a promise.

Chinmi!

What is it, Tao?

mething's.. mething's ppened the wn...

Chinmi! You've got to go there right now! Some drunks are causing trouble.
Huh!?
Is that so...?

Those three guys have come back looking for me!?

I won't stand for it!
They're beating up the old guy who runs the dumpling shop...

This is all my fault.
I've got the townsfolk into all sorts of trouble.

I'm going to the town!
You can't go alone!

There's more than three of them. There's about ten! With a huge man who looks like their boss.

They'll have to deal with me! Even if there are more of them, I started this on my own and that's how I'll finish it!!

Chinmi...
Think about what you're saying.

Maybe you will be able to get most of them...
...but **most** is not enough as long as one is left to finish you.

If you think you are responsible, you must find a solution, not a battle.
Chinmi, let's try and find an answer without fighting. Now is the time to honour your promise with a good plan.
Chinmi, don't try and solve this problem with force. Remember your promise. Prove it was sincere.

swoosh
screeee

We've been waiting for you, little monk!

How brave of you to come alone.

Are you all right?
Nothing too bad...

Little monk! Wouldn't you be better off worrying about yourself right now?

I'm sorr
for al
the
trouble
I've...
There's no need
to apologise.
Just get away
from here fast!
That
I cannot
do.
Little monk.
I hear
you've angered
my boys.
You've shamed
them in public.
This means
you have
dishonoured all
of us.
Is he
nuts or
what?
Does he have
any idea
what we're
going to do?

I haven't come here to fight. I've come to talk.
Did he say 'talk'?

This isn't what happened last time.
Maybe he knows when he's beaten, eh?

I apologise for dishonouring you. But you were drunk. Your behaviour was already bad.

Ooooh...I **get it.** We're such bums, you know. Just drifters. We should have realised.

So... apology accepted?

Did you **hear** that? What's the little priest up to?

9
You hurt three men and turned them into laughing stocks! You think saying sorry will make everything better?

10
Look, I've already apologised...

11
Yeah...I remember. You think you're head and shoulders above us, don't you?

12
So...get down on the ground where you belong...

14
Chinmi, show that you are sincere.

15
Are you really sorry, or was it all a lie?

My humble apologies!

I don't think you've got it quite right. Your head's still too high.

KLORK

If you want to do it properly, your head has to be here.

7
Chinmi...

8
Now! Let's try again, with feeling.

9
I regret any offence I may have caused...

10
What?
11
I can't hear you. Say it again.

12
I SAID I WAS SORRY! ALL RIGHT!?

13
You trying to burst my eardrums!!?
KADOOOSH

Did that hurt?
EH!?
SMAKK

You should be more careful...
KLOKK
KLONK

7
Stay alert...
g'lug

8
SPOOSH

9
Urgle

10
Don't mention it!
THWACK

11
Get up, sleepy head...

12
I said GET UP!!
DOOF!

13
Heh heh heh...

Ooooh...

I don't think I've got any spirit left at all...!!

This is terrible! They've gone too far!
One boy doesn't stand a chance.
eah...but
hat can
e do
about it?

Still think you can beat us?
Eh...?

I've got three friends here who want to have a word with you...

Are you still alive in there!?
THWAP SMAKK

SMAKK
THWACK
Oof
KLONK
CRUMP!

Damn...What am I supposed to do...?!

Now, that was a lot fairer, eh?

Crawl under my legs!
!

Crawl...
...under my legs.

Ryukai! Surely I don't have to endure this as well...?

Things can't possibly get worse than this.

If I do it...
Promise you'll drift on downstream and won't cause any more trouble here...?
Hhhr-hhr
Hhhr-hhr

Heh heh... yeah...OK!
Heh heh
heh

Is that a promise?

Get on with it!

Hahahaha

HA HA HA
HA HA
He's just like a little doggie!
Ha ha ha

This must be so embarrassing for you, little doggie.

Ha ha ha
ha ha ha

SMAK!
GASP!!

Forget about...
...my promise

I don't keep my word for dogs!

But you said you'd do it...
...if I crawled!

Well I've just changed my mind!!

SWISH
DIE!!

Chinmi has apologised a hundred times over.
AAAGH
Now you are dishonouring his sincerity.

Ryukai!!

Get up, Chinmi!

You've just crossed the line.
Paying them back in kind is your best medicine...

You up to it, Chinmi?
I'm ready!

R-U-M-B-L-E
Get 'em both!!
Pull no punches!
Gotcha!

ai-
ah!
THWACK

KRUMP
Hagh!
CRACK

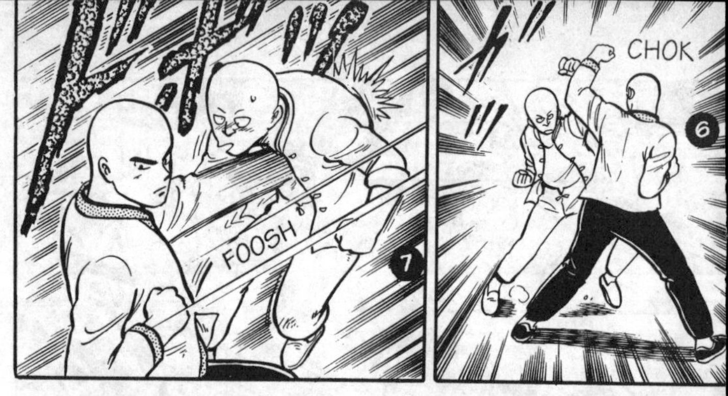
CHOK
FOOSH

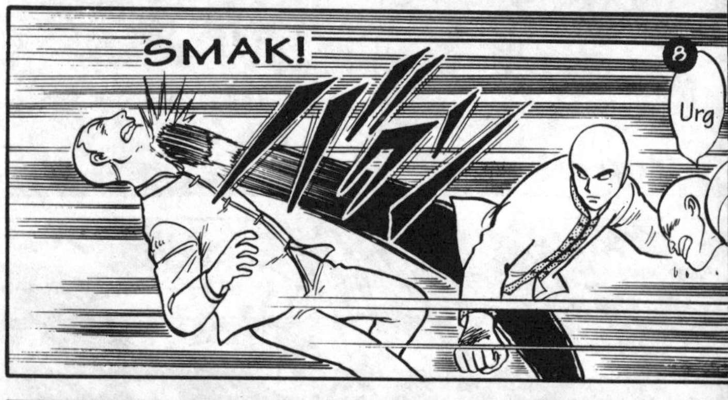
SMAK!
Urg

clump
SSWISH!
Oof

Hai-yah!
SWIP
Yagh!
THOK
SPLOOF!
BOFF!
A... Amazing!
Hooray!
Chinmi!
Chinmi

OK, Chinmi...
There's just one to go...
Oh...s
yo
remembe
Hee
Well boys, this world ain't going to miss either of you...
shik

Would you like him to yourself?
Yep.

Remember your fight with me.
If you want to defeat him you must use your Spirit... your Qi.
otcha!

Just one little monk?
Do you think you can beat me as well?
If you want to say sorry, now's your chance.

Well, well, well...
I think you're bluffing, you little pipsqueak...

Just try me!
Come on!

...

Well, fatso!

SHING
I'll get you!

SWOOSH!
ploing!
plat

swish
Swoosh!

SWOOSH
SWISH
Stand still, you...
Missed again!
I'll cut you in half!

DIE!!
SWOOSH

SPLUTCH!

Haha! Triple Punch!
Uh... oh...

That was the oldest trick in the book!!
KACHING
CHINMI!

You little squirt...
Chinmi! Use the KIAI! Use the battlecry!

Urgh...
chit
Kiai!
Kiai!!
KIAI!!

You won't get me this way!!

HA AA AA AA GH!!

PACHING!

!

Oh no! My Blue Dragon Blade!!

WHOOSH!
NOW!!

SPLUT

CRUNKKK

He did it!!
CHIN-MEEEE
Awesome! Awesome!
CHIN-MEEE
Well done, Chinmi!

clap-clap
Hooray!
CHIN-MEEEE!!
. . . .

I did it, Ryukai!
CHIN-MEEE

Yes, and the turning point was your battlecry. Well done, Chinmi!
CHIN-MEEE
CHIN-MEEE
clap-clap-clap-

The End of Chapter Three

PLING

Chapter Five
Chinmi's Battlecry

Zzzzz
くあ～っ

ガラガラ
creeeak

WAKE UP!
GET UP! IT'S MORNING!

Ooooh. I'm freezing!
It's cold eh!
Your breath is freezing.
So it is...
It's not even winter yet.
Morning training's going to get a lot harder.
Hey!
Yawn
Uh?
Let's help them get up.
zzzz
zzzzz
Yawn
Ready?
Teehee...
CHINMI! JIN TAN!
WAKE UF!!

12
Couldn't they have tried a different way?
13
Hah!
14
Yah!
15
Ryukai's taking the class today.
16
Good morning.
17
When it gets colder like this, you must not allow your Qi to become weaker!

Begin your warm-up!
Hah!
Hah!
Swip!
Swip!
Hah!
Hah!
Hah!
Hah!
Hah!
swip
swip
swip
swip
SWOOSH
Hah!!
Hah!!
THWAP
THWAP

Hah!
THWAP
SWIP
Eh? That was one too many...
Hah!
thwap
thwap-thwap-thwap
Hah!
thwap-thwap
swish
Hah!
thwap
Hah!
thwap-thwap
Hah!
Hah!
thwap-thwap-thwap

HAH!!
Hurgh!!
thwap thwap
thwap-thwap-thwap
thwap-thwap-
Hah!
Hah!
thwap-thwap-thwap-
HAAAARGH!!
I can't take it any more...
thwap-
thwap
flop
Right! Stop there!
Hhhr-hhr
Hhhr-hhr

Your battlecries are not good enough!
If you train without using the KIAI, you will never make any progress!
You must put the force of your shout behind each punch!
You are punching without first gathering the energy for your KIAI!

The force of just one punch with a KIAI, is worth five punches without it.

I will teach you how to control your Qi!
All of you! Follow me!

Is this the righ way to sit on stone?
Cold, isn't it?
What's he doing now?
Shhh!
Let us begin...

rustle

Wow...
His body is covered with scars...
I see how warrior training can be hard...
....

This is how you gather your Qi.
Now, watch carefully...

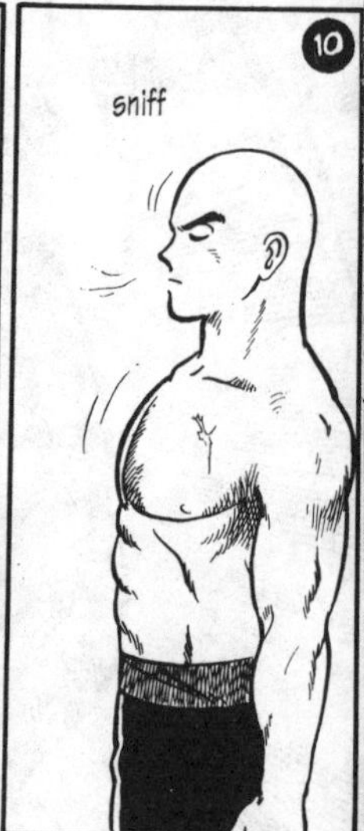
sniff

Haaaaaa

Rrrrrrr...

Hah!
SHING!

BWAAM

Haaaaaaaaaa

はあああ
HAAAAAAAAA
あああ
AAAAAAAAA

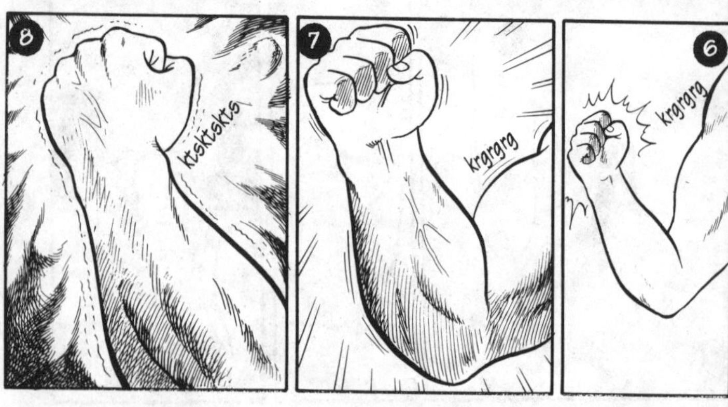
krgrgrg
krgrgrg
ktsktsktsktsts

Hah!
BWAAAM

sniff
Haaaaaah!!

BWOOM
Hoh!!
chik
phit
He snuffed out a candle just by doing that!
Wow...
Rrr rrr

hyakk
phut
thwap
thwap
Sshshshsh
Wh...what was that!?
Ah...
The power of his punch must have caused a blast of air...

So...
Now do you understand the difference the KIAI makes to the force of my punch?
The force flows from my stomach until my whole body is suffused with the KIAI.

As you ca see, there is a large difference between that punch, and a punch that does not use the KIAI.
The KIAI tightens all the muscles in your body.

Just one KIAI will alter the tension in your limbs.
Now.
Yes.
Do it...

Daaaaaa!!

Hah!

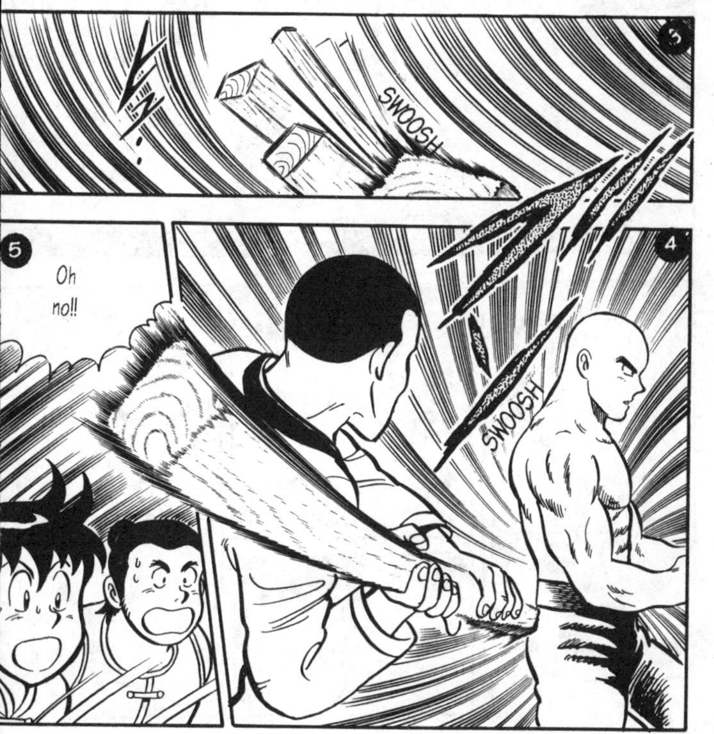
SWOOSH
SWOOSH
Oh no!!

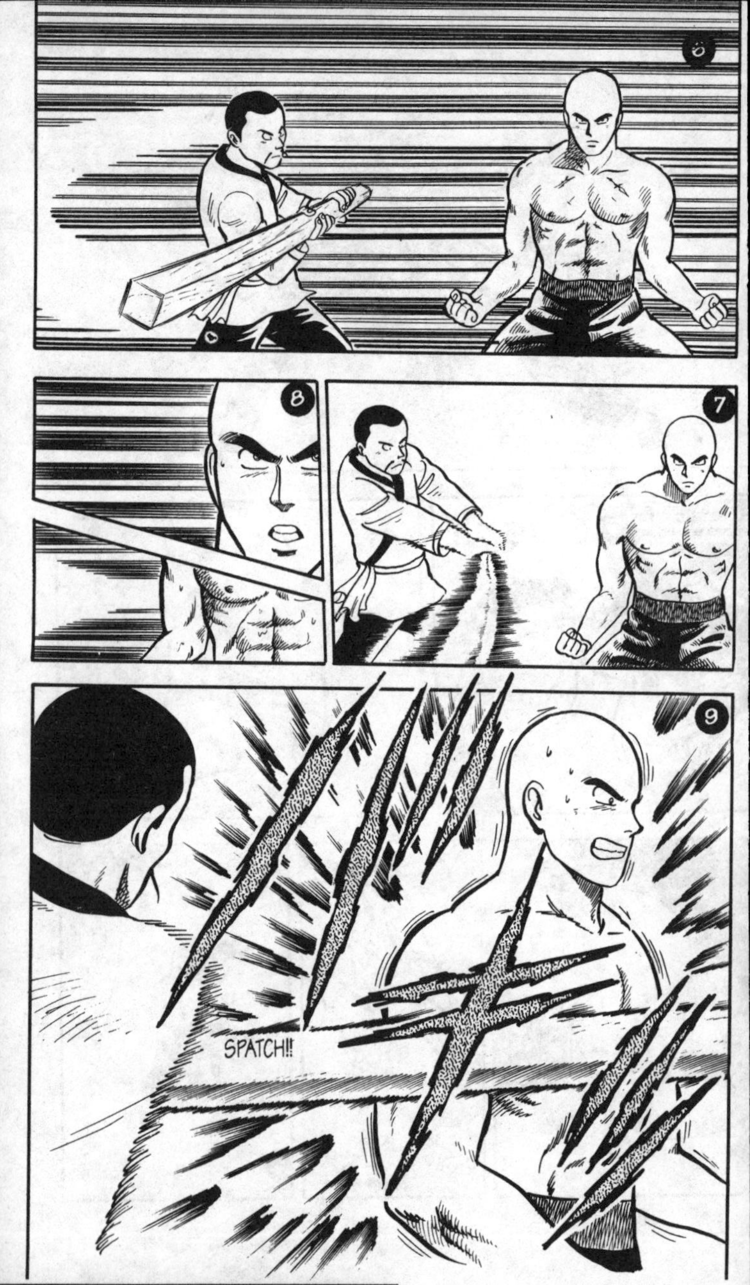
SPATCH!!

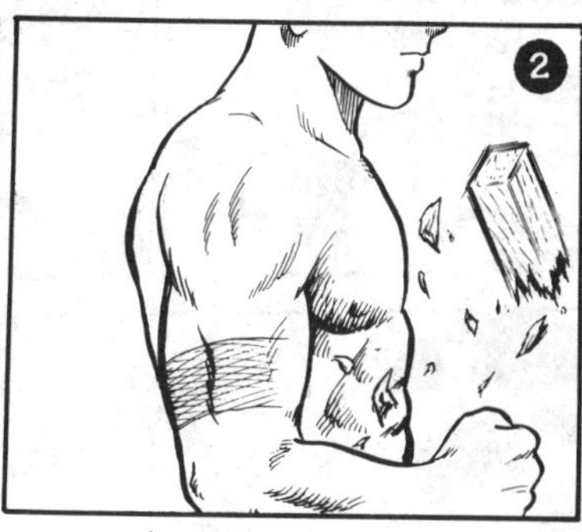

Gasp!!

The... the piece of wood...

clonk
clunk
It met with an immovable object!!

Wow...

Draw the force from your stomachs.
Haahh

Breathe in slowly to gather it.
Haaaa...

Hah!

shik shik
shik shik
Right now I'd love some sweet potatoes.
shik shik
Eeek eek.
What is it, Gokuwa?

Get back inside
Ah...ah...

ATCH-OOO!
Eek!

boing

Eek! Eek!

Eek! Eek!
You can see something over there?

Is she selling food!?

I've no money to buy sweet potatoes
I'm sorry, Gokuwa.

smakk

Oooh...
Hey! Are you hurt!?
Ahhh.
She's spilled her vegetables
Did you trip up? You should be more careful.
I'm sorry...

Eh?
I thought you were an old lady, but you're about my age!

I... I...
I've fallen on hard times, that's why.
ssh ssh

She's beautiful...
Ah! No! Don't worry!
Gokuwa!
donk
My name is Chinmi.
That's Gokuwa.

I'm Yang.

Are you all right, Yang?
Yes... thank you...

...

flup

That was so close...
flup

Yaaaay!

This way!!
Wait!
KRKRKRKRR
Yaaaay!
splot

CRUNCH

YANG!!
Hhhr-hhr

Why do I bother?

You look so tired.

I'm fine...

You're boiling!
You should be in bed.

I can't! I have to sell all these vegetables today, or...
.....

OK!

I'll help you out.

What am I going to do about Chinmi...?
He's gone off to play with Gokuwa again.

Fresh veg! Fresh veg!
Get your luver-ly vegies here!
Isn't that Chinmi?
The guy from the dumpling shop...
That's him...
I'll buy some.
Cheapest in town! Buy now... er...pay now!
It's Chinmi!
Look! A monkey.
Give the money to Gokuwa! Here's your veg!
Eeek! £$
Cheap at twice the price!
Thankin' you, ta!
Have a nice day!

Thank you so much for helping me...
Heheh! Don't mention it!

That money we've just made is very important.

Great.

Grand-father and I...
...have been working two years to get this money.

You mean I've helped your whole family? Get away!

....

That's my house up there.

Well, here you are.
There's no way I can ever repay you for your help.

Aw...it was nothing.

Thank you, Chinmi.

Right Gokuwa, let's go.

Thank you...
Chinmi...

Grand-father...

I've brought the...

Yang...

Grandfather...!!

Yang... I do hope you've brought the money.

Yang...

What have you done to him!?

chink

There! That's the whole amount we owe.
I don't want to see either of you in this house again.

Well...
That's not good enough.

Eh!?

I think you'll find you've forgotten the interest, my dear!

You're lying!
借用証
金○○也

Look at the bond!!

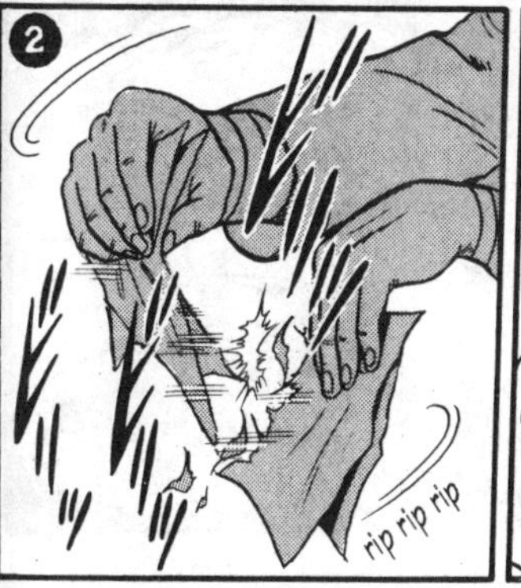
rip rip rip

flak

Gasp!

The interest is ten times this amount.

That's not fair!!

Oh dear...
How much is this worth, I wonder...
KRASH
Not much, I bet.
SMASH
Stop it!

Please stop!
SMASH

Shut up!!

CRASH

If you can't find the money, Yang...
I'll be back for you!

Not those! They belonged to my parents!
SMASH

AAAAaah

How could you be so cruel!?

I can hear bullies at work!!

I heard everything! You swine!
How could you be so inhuman!!

Chinmi!!

What are you going to do about it, kid!?
Send you home.

And if we refuse to go...
Step outside!!

Chinmi ...!
Make mincemeat out of him.
スィー
swit
!?
I've never seen that move before.

swoosh
thwap
swish
You can do better than that...
swoop

swip
swish

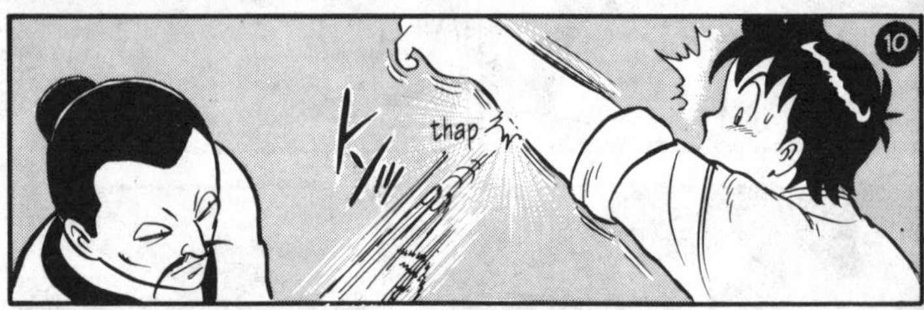
thap

throb
AAA
agh!

swip

I can't move it...!!

What have you done!?
Feels good, eh?

It's not over yet!
swish

thap

That was the Kidney Point!

!!
chak

Ah! My arms
flop

And now they're both not working, eh?

Now what will you do?

How about this!?
thok

うわあああ
WAAAAAGH!!

kachunk

My body's frozen!!
Heh heh heh. That was another Pressure Point!

The human body has 708 points which lead to 40 major organs. A tap at the right place can immobilise. But you have to know the right place!

That is my Kung Fu...
The POINTING FIST!!

This little brat hasn't got a hope of getting up...
Thanks to my Pointing Fist.

SMAKK
Got that?!

It's curtains for you!!
SMAK
CRASH
THWAP

You little brat!!
SMAKK
KLOKK
Stop it! You'll kill him!

End of Book Three

Published in Great Britain 1995
by Bloomsbury Children's Books
2 Soho Square, London W1V 5DE

First published in Japan 18 February 1985 and
as at 20 July 1994, reprinted 29 times
by Kodansha, Tokyo.
English publication rights arranged through Kodansha

English Edition
Translated by Jonathan Clements

A CIP catalogue record for this book
is available from the British Library

ISBN 0-7475-2098-4
10 9 8 7 6 5 4 3 2 1

Printed and bound in Great Britain by
William Clowes (Beccles) Ltd, Beccles and London